Colors

Program Authors
Richard L. Allington
Camille Blachowicz
Ronald L. Cramer
Patricia M. Cunningham
G. Yvonne Pérez
Constance Frazier Robinson
Sam Leaton Sebesta
Richard G. Smith
Robert J. Tierney

Instructional Consultant
John C. Manning

Program Consultants
Nancy Apodaca
Alice Parra

Critic Readers
Elaine K. Cannon
Linda Hassett
Sister Carleen Reck
Norma Rodríguez
Jane Sasaki
Michael M. Sheridan

**Scott, Foresman
and Company**

Editorial Offices:
Glenview, Illinois

Regional Offices:
Sunnyvale, California
Tucker, Georgia
Glenview, Illinois
Oakland, New Jersey
Dallas, Texas

Scott, Foresman Reading: An American Tradition

Acknowledgments

Text
"Yellow" from *Away and Ago* by David McCord. Copyright ©
1974 by David McCord. Reprinted by permission of Little,
Brown and Company.

Artists
Michael Adams, pages 50–55; Elizabeth Allen, pages 5–9;
Patti Boyd, pages 44–49; Julie Durrell, page 64;
Carl Kock, pages 12–17, 67–70; Cindy Maniates, pages 32–37;
Elizabeth Miles, pages 56–63; Yoshi Miyake, pages 18–23;
Georgia Shola, pages 10–11; Justin Wagner, pages 24–25, 38–43;
Jack Wallen, page 66

Freelance Photography
Creative Design (props), pages 32–37;
Michael Goss, pages 26–31, 32–37

Cover Artist
Georgia Shola

ISBN: 0-673-71504-3

2345678910–VHJ–96959493929190898887

Contents

Stories by:

Caron Lee Cohen

Maythee Jensen Kantar

Liane Onish

Sallie Runck

Mary Shuter

Betty von Glahn

Joe and Mom Paint

Joe likes to paint with yellow paint.

Is Joe painting a yellow cat?

Is Joe painting yellow boxes and bags?

What is Joe painting?

It is a yellow duck!

Joe likes to paint with blue paint.

What is Joe painting for Duck?

Is Joe painting a blue hat?

Is it a blue book to read?

Joe has painted a blue pond.
The yellow duck can swim in
a blue pond!
Mom comes to see Joe.
Mom likes Duck and the pond.
Mom may want to paint.

Mom likes to paint with red paint.

What is Mom painting for Duck?

Is it a red flower?

Is it a red dog?

It is a red van!
Duck has a red van and
Mom has a red van.
Mom wants a good van like the
van Duck has!

Looking Ahead

Blue, Yellow, and Green

Rob says, "You like to paint.
Here is a white brush and
a paint box."

Gus looks at the white brush and the
paints.

Gus says, "I like your paints
and brushes.
May I paint with your
paints and brushes?"

Rob says, "You may."

Rob gives brushes and paints to Gus.

Rob says, "You may dip a brush
into this red paint.
You may dip a brush into this
blue paint.
You may dip a brush into this
yellow paint."

Gus dips a brush into
the blue paint.
Gus paints a blue pond.

Gus wants to paint a frog.

Gus does not have green paint.

Gus dips a brush into the
yellow paint.

Gus paints a frog on the blue pond.

This frog is green, not yellow!

This is a color trick!

Gus wants to tell Rob!

Gus says, "I have a color trick.
I painted a yellow frog on
a blue pond.
This frog is green!
Blue and yellow make green!"

Rob says, "What a good trick!
You take yellow and blue paint
to make green paint."

The Ball Trick

Rose and Ana see Sam.

Sam says, "I like your cat.
I like your ball, Rose."

Rose says, "Can you tell I am Rose?"

Sam says, "I can tell!
You like cats and ducks.
Ana likes dogs."

Rose says to Ana, "Sam can tell
I am Rose.
Sam can tell you are Ana.
I want to play a trick on Sam.
Sam likes tricks."

Ana says, "I will help you.
You and I will play a trick on Sam."

Ana says, "Here is white paint.
I will dip the brush into the
white paint.
I will put white paint on the dog.
You put white paint on the duck.
Sam will not see the duck and
the dog."

21

Ana says, "I will paint Rose on my ball.

You paint Ana on your ball."

Rose says, "What a good trick!
Sam will say I am you!
Sam will say you are me!"

Sam comes to play.

Sam says to Rose, "Will you play ball with me, Rose?"

Rose says, "I am Ana!
Look at my ball!"

Sam says, "You wanted to trick me!
I can tell you are Rose.
You have the yellow cat!"

Frog Wants Fun

DUCK 1: Duck, can you tell
this frog wants fun?
What games can Frog play?
Can Frog jump and run?

DUCK 2: Frog can jump and run.

Frog can read a green book.

Frog can pick a flower.

Come take a look!

DUCK 1: Frog can play with a ball.

Frog can reach up and clap.

Frog can make a red fan.

Frog can tap, tap, tap.

FROG: I am not sad.

I will jump and run.

Come play a game.

Playing is fun!

A Good Mom

Pat and Val see Mom.

Pat says, "You look good, Mom.
I like your pin.
Where are you going?"

Mom says, "I am going to eat.
Have fun, girls."

Pat says, "Mom is a good mom.
She reads books to you and me."

Val says, "She takes me to the pond.
She helps you with games.
What can you and I do for Mom?"

Val says, "Mom likes pins.
A pin will make Mom happy.
I can make a pin for Mom.
Do you want to help me make a pin?"

Pat says, "I do!
I want to put flowers on the pin.
I will see what I can find."

Pat says, "See what I have!
This will make flowers for the pin.
I want the flowers to be
blue and yellow."

Pat says, "I want red and
white flowers.
It can be a blue, yellow, red, and
white pin!"

Val makes blue and yellow flowers.
Pat makes red and white flowers.

Val says, "This will be a good pin."

Pat says, "I like the pin.
Mom will be happy with it.
Here comes Mom!"

Val and Pat give the pin to Mom.
Mom puts on the big pin.
She likes the blue, yellow, red,
green, and white pin.

Mom says, "This is a good pin!"

Val says, "This is a good pin for a
good mom!"

Colors for a Hat

Pig said, "Where are you going?"

Duck said, "I am going for a swim.
Come for a swim, Pig."

Pig said, "Can't you tell I am sick?
A sick pig can't swim."

Duck said to Chicken, "Pig is sad.
Pig is sick.
What can I do to help make Pig happy?
I have it!
I will look into my hat boxes and
find a hat for Pig.
Come help me."

Duck and Chicken looked at hat boxes.
Chicken picked a big hat for Pig.

She said, "This big hat will be good.
Where can I find colors to put on
the hat?
A hat for a sick pig has to
have colors.
Colors will make Pig happy."

Chicken picked big red and yellow
flowers for the hat.

Duck picked out green, blue, red, and
yellow pins.

She said, "You have flowers, and
I have pins.
I will pin the flowers to the hat!"

Duck put the pins on the flowers.
She put the flowers on the hat.

She said, "The hat looks good!"

Chicken said, "Pig will be happy.
Where is Pig?
I will go see where Pig is."

Duck and Chicken ran to see Pig.

Chicken said, "This hat is for you.
See what flowers and colored pins
can do!
Do you like your hat?"

Pig said, "I do!
A sick pig can be happy!"

A Girl Likes Colors

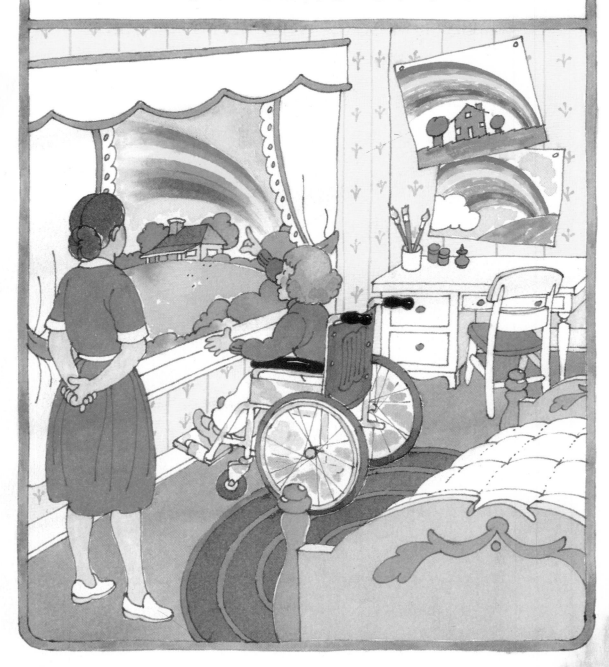

Duck Wants to Play

Duck said, "I like to play in snow.

I will get Bear.

Bear likes to play in snow.

It will be fun to play with Bear."

Duck ran to get Bear.

Duck said, "Come play in the snow."

Bear said, "I <u>am</u> playing in the snow."

Duck said, "Where are you?"

Bear said, "You passed me."

Duck said, "Where can Bear be?
I can't see a white bear in the
white snow.
Here comes Dog.
Dog can help me find Bear."

Duck said, "I want to play with Bear.
I passed Bear in the snow.
I can't see a white bear in the
white snow."

Dog said, "I can't see a white
bear in the white snow."

Duck said, "Where are you, Bear?"

Dog said, "Where are you, Bear?"

Bear said, "I am right here with you!
You passed me in the snow.
I think I can help you find me.
Pass me your cap, Dog."

Dog passed the cap to Bear, and Bear reached for the cap.
Bear put on the cap.

Dog said, "I get it!
Good thinking, Bear!"

Duck said, "I can see a red cap in white snow!
I can tell where Bear is!"

What Colors Do You See?

It is **fall.**

Leaves are colored in the fall.

What colors do you see?

Do you see the red leaves?

Do you see the yellow leaves?

Do you see the green leaves?

Leaves fall in the fall!
The red and yellow leaves fall on
a boy.
The falling leaves make the
boy happy.

The boy likes to see the
leaves fall.
The boy likes the red, green, and
yellow leaves.
The boy thinks the colored leaves
look good in the fall.
The boy thinks fall is fun.

The boy wants to get leaves.
The boy wants to play with leaves.
The boy picks up red, yellow, and
green leaves.
Where will the boy put the leaves?
The boy will put the leaves into
a tub.

The boy puts the green leaves
into the tub.
The boy puts the yellow leaves and
the red leaves into the tub.
What will the boy do with the leaves?

The boy gets into the tub.

The boy jumps!

Leaves in a tub can be fun.

The boy thinks fall is fun.

What do you think?

What Color Is Good?

This tan bird does not like tan.

She says, "I do not look good in tan.
I want to look good."

The tan bird sees yellow feathers.

She says, "I do like yellow."

She picks up yellow feathers.
She puts on the yellow feathers.

adapted from Aesop's "The Vain Jackdaw"

The tan bird sees blue feathers.

She says, "I do like blue."

The tan bird picks up the
blue feathers.
She puts on the blue feathers.

The tan bird sees red feathers.

She says, "I do like red."

She picks up the red feathers.
She puts on the red feathers.

The tan bird says, "I look good!"

A yellow bird sees the tan bird.

The yellow bird says, "I see my feathers."

The yellow bird takes the yellow feathers.

A blue bird sees the tan bird.

The blue bird says, "I see
my feathers."

The blue bird takes the blue feathers.

A red bird sees the tan bird.

The red bird says, "I see
my feathers."

The red bird takes the red feathers.

A green bird sees the tan bird.

The green bird says, "You look sad."

The tan bird says to him, "I do not like tan."

The green bird says, "I think you look good in tan.
Sit and look."

The tan bird sits.

She looks at the tan feathers.

She looks and looks and looks.

The green bird is right!

The tan bird says, "I <u>do</u> look good in tan!"

She is happy.

To be read by the teacher

Yellow

by David McCord

Green is go,
and red is stop,
and yellow is peaches
with cream on top.

Earth is brown,
and blue is sky;
yellow looks well
on a butterfly.

Clouds are white,
black, pink or mocha;
yellow's a dish of
tapioca.

Looking Back

To be read by the teacher

Thinking About the Book

Color is important in this book.

1. What color trick does Gus learn?

2. How do colors make the sick pig happy?

3. Why can't Duck and Dog find Bear in the snow?

4. Why does the tan bird want colors?

Books to Read

Do You Want To Be My Friend?
by Eric Carle

Little Mouse wants to play.
Does Little Mouse get to play?
Read the book and see.

is it red? is it yellow? is it blue?
by Tana Hoban

Do you like red and blue and yellow?
Look for the colors in this book.

I Like Things
by Margaret Hillert

A girl likes books and fall leaves.
See what the girl likes to find.

Ways to Do Schoolwork

1. Draw a picture.

2. Trace the letter.

3. Write the letter.

4. Underline the word.

5. Circle the word.

6. Write the word.

7. Circle the picture.

8. Put an <u>X</u> in the box.

9. Fill in the circle.

10. Use a typewriter.

11. Use a computer.

12. Use a tape recorder.

Word List

Unit 1

says 12

white 12

brush 12

dip 14

this 14

color 16

trick 16

tell 16

fan 25

Unit 2

pin 26

where 26

she 27

do 27

happy 28

be 29

pig 32

said 32

sick 32

chicken 33